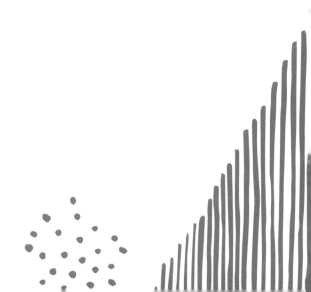

Treasured Journal: An Interactive Experience for A Tween Girl & Her Mom
Published by Orange, a division of The reThink Group, Inc.
5870 Charlotte Lane, Suite 300
Cumming, GA 30040 U.S.A.

The Orange logo is a registered trademark of The reThink Group, Inc.

Other Orange products are available online and direct from the publisher. Visit our website at www.ThinkOrange.com for more resources like these.

ISBN: 978-1-63570-091-6

Authors: Courtney DeFeo and Parent Cue
Contributing Writer: Holly Crawshaw
Editorial Team: Sherry Surratt, Karen Wilson, Tim Walker
Art Direction: Sharon van Rossum
Project Manager: Nate Brandt

Printed in the United States of America

First Edition 2019
2 3 4 5 6 7 8 9 10 11

09/07/2021

Treasured

JOURNAL

AN INTERACTIVE EXPERIENCE
FOR A TWEEN GIRL & HER MOM

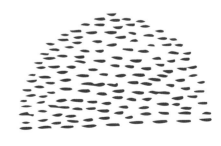

Dear Treasured Girl,

Welcome to the *Treasured Journal*! This journal will help you think through things that almost every girl your age is facing right now. And you know what's cool? Your mom has faced these things, too. She's the perfect person to talk to about these topics—from one girl to another.

In these pages, you'll find six topics to talk about, dream about, and create. Over the next six weeks, you'll have fun discovering more about what God has to say about these things:

Week 1: IDENTITY

Week 2: YOUR BODY

Week 3: EMOTIONS

Week 4: FRIENDSHIPS

Week 5: TECHNOLOGY

Week 6: FAITH

If you miss a day, it's okay! You can go through each topic at your own pace. The best thing about this journal is it's yours. So grab your favorite markers or colored pencils and make it uniquely you. Most importantly, have fun!

Everything is more fun with friends, so if you aren't part of a Treasured Group already, invite a group of friends and their moms to go through the journal together as part of the *Treasured Study*, found at **ParentCueStore.org**.

Week 1:

IDENTITY

BE AMAZED BY HOW GOD MADE YOU

˜Verse:

"How you made me is amazing
and wonderful. I praise you for that.
What you have done is wonderful.
I know that very well."

Psalm 139:14 NIrV

What do you think of when you hear the word *identity*?

- ★ Huh? Identi-what? What's that mean?
- ★ It'd be super cool to be a spy with a secret identity.
- ★ That time someone stole your mom's credit card number and she reported it as identity theft.

What else does the word identity make you think about?

_____

_____

_____

_____

_____

The simplest way to define identity is this—

WHATEVER UNIQUE CHARACTERISTICS YOU HAVE THAT SEPARATE YOU FROM SOMEONE ELSE.

In other words, whatever makes you *you*—that's your identity.

Your identity is . . .

* THE SOUND OF YOUR LAUGH.
* YOUR FINGERPRINT.
* HOW YOUR SECOND TOE IS LONGER
  OR SHORTER THAN YOUR BIG TOE.
* YOUR LOVE OF LLAMAS.
* YOUR HANDWRITING.
* HOW YOUR EYES TEAR UP WHEN YOU SEE
  A PUPPY THAT NEEDS A HOME.

Your identity is the hundred little things that make you different from someone else.

Using colored pencils, pens, or markers fill in the "grooves" of the thumbprint on the next page with all the things that are unique about you. Where were you born? How many siblings do you have? Favorite sport? Hair color? Write in all the things that make you unique—just like your one-of-a kind thumbprint.

Day 2

Did you know the Bible has a lot to say about your identity? It does! Because the most important part of your identity has nothing to do with you. It has to do with the One who created your identity.

Check this out:

"HOW YOU MADE ME IS AMAZING AND WONDERFUL. I PRAISE YOU FOR THAT. WHAT YOU HAVE DONE IS WONDERFUL. I KNOW THAT VERY WELL."

PSALM 139:14 NIRV

The speaker in this psalm is talking to the Creator—to God. Underline the words *amazing* and *wonderful* in the first sentence.

What are some things that God created that you think are *amazing* and *wonderful*?

_____

_____

_____

_____

_____

_____

_____

_____

Now, add *you* to the list.

_____

It's true! God made us in an amazing and wonderful way.

Now, ask your mom to sit down with you for a few minutes and take turns answering or drawing your thoughts on the next page. (Leave your phones/tablets in another room so you can concentrate without distractions!)

I AM AMAZING BECAUSE . . .

(Write or draw a few words that describe why you are amazing.)

MY MOM THINKS I AM AMAZING BECAUSE . . .

(Ask your mom to fill out this part.)

You were created with intention. You are unique and one-of-a-kind. Everything about you was formed on *purpose*, from your head down to your toes—even your personality.

Put a ⭐ beside the statements that are true about your identity (the unique things that make you *you*).

- ∿ I AM MADE FOR THE STAGE. I FEEL SO AT HOME IN FRONT OF AN AUDIENCE.
- ∿ I AM MADE FOR THE SPELLING BEE.
- ∿ I AM MADE FOR THE SOCCER STATE CHAMPIONSHIP.
- ∿ I AM MADE FOR SLIME. I'D MAKE IT ALL DAY LONG.
- ∿ I AM MADE FOR MAKING NEW FRIENDS.
- ∿ I AM MADE TO BE IN MY ROOM WITH A BOOK UNDER THE COVERS.
- ∿ I AM MADE TO CREATE AND CRAFT AND GET MESSY.
- ∿ I AM MADE TO BE OUTSIDE. BEING IN NATURE MAKES ME FEEL ALIVE.
- ∿ I AM MADE FOR SPORTS. I LOVE COMPETING.
- ∿ I AM MADE TO DANCE AND JUMP AROUND.
- ∿ I AM MADE TO LOVE ON OTHER PEOPLE.
- ∿ I AM MADE FOR MUSIC. I LIKE TO PLAY IT, SING IT, AND LISTEN TO IT.
- ∿ I AM MADE TO ENJOY LOTS OF PEOPLE—I LIKE THEM ALL AROUND ME.
- ∿ I AM MADE TO ENJOY A FEW CLOSE FRIENDS.
- ∿ I AM MADE TO HELP OTHERS. I FEEL BEST WHEN I AM SUPPORTING A FRIEND.
- ∿ I AM MADE TO BE WITH MY FAMILY. THEY ARE MY HAPPY PLACE.
- ∿ I AM MADE TO BE A GAMER. NO ONE HAS BETTER THUMBS!

Day 3

Last time we talked about the One who created us—God! We said that the way God made us is amazing and wonderful. We said the fact that we were made by God is the most important part of our identity.

But sometimes that's hard to remember, right? Especially on the days our hair won't cooperate or we don't make the lacrosse team or we flunk that prepositions test . . . again.

On these days, we find ourselves feeling not so amazing or wonderful. On these days, it can feel like everyone around us has or does something better than we do. That's called *comparison*—when we measure ourselves against other people.

Here's the thing: All people—especially girls—compare themselves to others. We do this when it comes to who is the funniest, most athletic, the best singer, or who has the most friends. But comparison always leaves us feeling worse about ourselves. It leaves us feeling less than, not good enough, or like we don't measure up.

This is a measuring stick. Think of a few ways that girls—any girl—might feel like they have to measure up to someone or something. Write them on the ruler (examples: grades, clothes, Instagram likes, etc.).

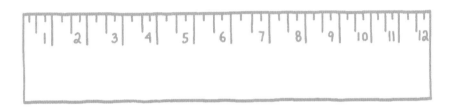

The truth is that we were *all* made with important and unique abilities and features. God thought about you as He made you. He thought about your smile, your freckles, your trouble with spelling, your quirky personality, and the cool way you can curl your tongue.

Now grab some colored pencils, pens, or markers and color in this week's verse on the next page.

"How you made me is amazing and wonderful. I praise you for that. What you have done is wonderful. I know that very well."

Psalm 139:14 NIrV

We've talked about how difficult it can be when we compare ourselves to others. No one likes feeling like they don't measure up. So how do we keep from doing it? How do we believe what God says about us is true?

We do what this verse says!

Even when we don't feel like praising God's creation, we can still praise the Creator!

Here's the deal. When you meet an artist, you praise the artist for what they created. You praise the work of their hand. That is what the person who wrote our verse does. The praise isn't based on how well the artwork measures up against other pieces of art. Their artwork is praised because of the one who created it!

You don't always feel like artwork. It's hard to praise one piece of art when you like another piece of art better. But you can fight comparison by doing what the psalmist did. He praised the artist.

"I PRAISE YOU FOR THAT. WHAT YOU HAVE DONE IS WONDERFUL. I KNOW THAT VERY WELL."

Breaking the measuring stick, the habit of comparison, starts with thanking God for how He created you.

THANK YOU FOR MY NOSE.

THANK YOU FOR MY STRONG LEGS.

THANK YOU FOR MY LOUD PERSONALITY.

Thank God for three things unique about you:

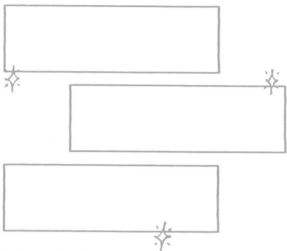

Then, thank God for the way He created anyone you're comparing yourself to.

Thank you for making her so fun.
Thank you for making her with such pretty hair.
Thank you for making her so good at soccer.

YOU BREAK THE MEASURING STICK BY BEING GRATEFUL FOR THE WAY GOD MADE YOU.

And when you realize how wonderful your Creator is, you will begin to believe how amazing He made you to be.

Turn the page back to the measuring stick you wrote on and write in big letters : **I AM AMAZING!**

Day 4

Complete the following sentences:

1. ONE SKILL OR TALENT I HAVE IS

_____ .

2. I AM REALLY GOOD AT

_____ .

3. ONE THING I REALLY LIKE ABOUT MY BODY IS

_____ .

4. SOMETHING UNIQUE ABOUT ME IS

_____ .

5. I'VE GOTTEN BETTER AT

_____ .

Hopefully, you'll also get better at celebrating your identity—the things that make you *you*.

One of the best ways to fight measuring ourselves against others is by reminding ourselves of the truth that we were made on purpose by a God who has big plans for our lives. Grab your Bible or open a Bible app (the NIrV translation is a good one to use). Look up the following verses and then write them down:

EPHESIANS 2:10

JEREMIAH 29:11

MATTHEW 10:31

WHEN YOU FEEL LIKE YOU DON'T BELONG,

READ EPHESIANS 2:10

YOU WERE CREATED TO BELONG TO JESUS.

WHEN YOU WONDER WHAT GOD THINKS ABOUT YOU,

READ JEREMIAH 29:11

GOD THINKS GOOD THOUGHTS TOWARD YOU.

WHEN YOU DON'T FEEL VALUABLE,

READ MATTHEW 10:31

YOU ARE CALLED WORTHY BY GOD.

Day 5

Invite your mom for some hang-out time and complete the following activities together.

Activity 1

Ask your mom to play a game of **THIS or THAT** with you. Take turns and circle which you like better in each pair. Use different colored pens or markers so you can keep track of each other's answers!

VANILLA or CHOCOLATE

JEANS or DRESSES

PUPPIES or KITTENS

BEACH or MOUNTAIN

MOVIE NIGHT or SPORTS NIGHT

FAST FOOD or FANCY

MYSTERY MOVIE or COMEDY

GETTING UP EARLY or GOING TO BED LATE

CLEANING YOUR ROOM or DOING HOMEWORK

CHOCOLATE or GUMMY WORMS

Activity 2

Discuss together . . .

- ★ **WHAT CAN YOU DO WELL THAT MOST PEOPLE CAN'T?**
- ★ **WHAT'S A HOBBY OR SKILL YOU'D LIKE TO WORK ON?**
- ★ **WHAT'S A GOOD WAY TO HANDLE FEELINGS OF JEALOUSY OR THOUGHTS ABOUT NOT MEASURING UP?**

Activity 3

Choose one of the following activities to create together on the next page. You might want to each choose one and then share them with each other.

1. YOU ARE A FASHION DESIGNER. Grab some colored pencils or markers and create your dream outfit. What would you wear to school, work, or around the house every day if you could? Don't forget to design the exact look of the shoe, the skirt or the jeans, the shirt or sweatshirt. Choose colors that are you.

2. YOU ARE A DAY DREAMER. If you could design your dream day, what would it look like? Would you hang out with your friends or family? Would you spend a whole day at home, in a favorite store, or go to a faraway place? Dream big and design the day that would make you smile!

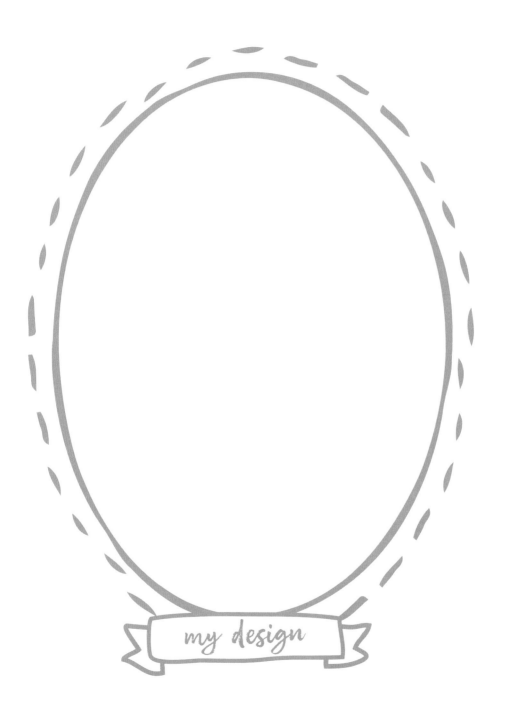
my design

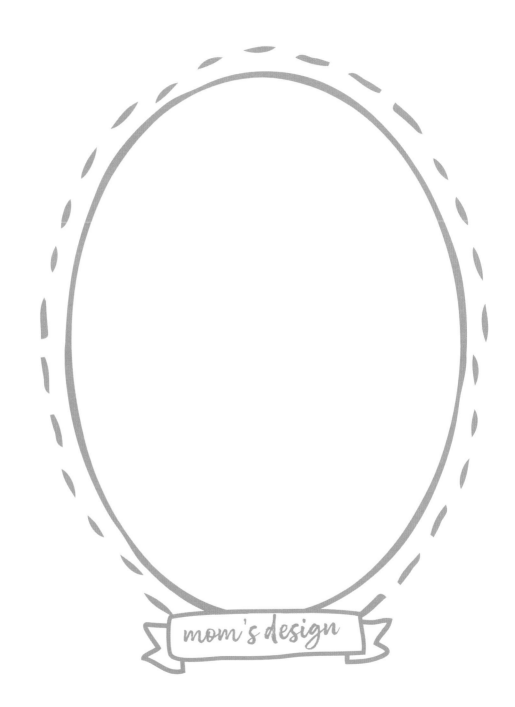

mom's design

From One Treasured Girl to Another

Have you ever wondered why she has blond hair and you don't? Or she is better at soccer than you are? Does God love her more than me? Why is she so much more athletic than I am? You were made in God's image. He made you an identity, a certain one, just for you. Many people may tell you to "be yourself." Sounds pretty familiar, right? But you think, *Why? They're better at more stuff than I am, or they're prettier than I am.* But are they? First Samuel 16:7 says: *"The Lord said to Samuel, 'Do not look at his appearance or on the height of your stature because I have rejected him for the Lord sees not as man sees: Man looks only outward appearance, but the Lord looks on the heart'"* (ESV).

You are gifted in so many ways. Some you don't even know yet.

God made you the way you are. If He wanted you to be the fastest girl in class, you would be. God made you to be you!

Which means there is a purpose that you are you. You are meant to do something.

There's a story about a girl. She had beautiful brown eyes, but she wanted bright blue eyes. One night she stood in front of her mirror and prayed that when she woke up she would have blue eyes. Then that next morning, she woke up and looked in the mirror and she still had brown eyes. She wondered why God had not given her blue eyes.

When she grew up, she heard of a country where children were taken away from their families. She wanted to go save those children and take them to safety. She decided that she would do it. She bathed in coffee to turn her skin the right color. Then she went to the country, disguised herself as a buyer, and went to look for the kids. She escaped with the kids and helped saved their lives. If she had had blue eyes she would have been noticed immediately. God gave her brown eyes for a reason. And God made you *you* for a reason.

Don't let other girls tell you you're not pretty enough or cool enough. You are a star shining in the world. Be kind and you will shine—I promise! Daniel 12:3 says: *"Those who are wise will shine like the brightness of the heavens, and those who lead many to righteousness, like the stars forever and ever."*

Ansley Allen Middleton, Age 10

We'd love to hear from you too! Submit your devotional writings to **TreasuredGirlz.com** *in the contact section.*

Notes

_____

_____

_____

_____

_____

_____

_____

_____

_____

_____

_____

_____

_____

_____

_____

Week 2:

YOUR BODY

BE IN CHARGE OF YOUR BODY

⌒ Verse:

"Don't you know that your bodies are temples of the Holy Spirit? The Spirit is in you, and you have received the Spirit from God. You do not belong to yourselves. Christ has paid the price for you. So use your bodies in a way that honors God."

1 Corinthians 6:19-20 NIrV

Day 1

What do you think will be the best age ever? _____

What do you think will be the best part about being that age? List a few reasons:

1. _____

2. _____

3. _____

It's fun to dream about the new things you'll get to do and experience as you grow up.

But there's *one* thing you can start doing now. And it's a pretty big thing.

Look at our verse for the week on the left. Underline the last sentence: *So use your bodies in a way that honors God.*

Did you know that you are in charge of your body? That may not sound like a big deal, but it is. It is a **HUGE** deal, actually. Because you are the only person on the planet who can be in charge of your body.

Think about it. What are some things you do for your body every day? Check all that are true for you and add your own to the list:

- ☐ BRUSH YOUR TEETH
- ☐ WASH YOUR FACE
- ☐ PUT ON DEODORANT
- ☐ EXERCISE
- ☐ GET DRESSED
- ☐ WEAR A HELMET ON YOUR BIKE
- ☐ EAT
- ☐ DRINK WATER
- ☐ GO FOR A WALK
- ☐ PUT ON A SEATBELT
- ☐ _____
- ☐ _____
- ☐ _____
- ☐ _____

You're in charge of keeping your body well-fed and making sure it doesn't smell like a garbage can. You're in charge of giving your body enough rest. You're in charge of taking *care* of your body, being kind to your body, even protecting your body.

Sure, there are things your parents are still in control of when it comes to helping you take care of your body, but ultimately, you are in charge of your body.

Now, find some time with your mom and ask her to sit down with you for a few minutes and take turns thinking about some of your favorite things when it comes to taking care of your body. (Leave your phones/tablets in another room so you can concentrate without distractions!)

What's your favorite . . .

* SCENT OF LOTION? _____

* WAY TO GET EXERCISE? _____

* BREAKFAST MEAL? _____

* SNACK? _____

* HAIRSTYLE? _____

* BATH OR SHOWER? _____

Day 2

During our last time together, we talked about the idea that you are in charge of your body.

What are some other things you're in charge of or responsible for? (Think about school, practice, chores, pets).

1. _____

2. _____

3. _____

Since you're already in charge of things like taking out the trash, feeding the family fish, and remembering to do your homework, you know an important thing about growing up.

Growing up means more fun experiences, but it also means more responsibilities.

So—what's the big deal? Why should you care so much about your body?

Who cares if you . . .

* **EAT AN ENTIRE BAG OF SOUR SKITTLES®
  BEFORE BED?**
* **STAY AWAKE ALL NIGHT ON YOUR
  FAVORITE APP?**
* **SKIP THE SHOWER FOR A DAY OR FOUR?**

What would you think if someone told you *God* cares? He does. Read this:

> "DON'T YOU KNOW THAT YOUR BODIES ARE TEMPLES OF THE HOLY SPIRIT? THE SPIRIT IS IN YOU, AND YOU HAVE RECEIVED THE SPIRIT FROM GOD. YOU DO NOT BELONG TO YOURSELVES. CHRIST HAS PAID THE PRICE FOR YOU. SO USE YOUR BODIES IN A WAY THAT HONORS GOD."
>
> **1 CORINTHIANS 6:19-20 NIRV**

Okay, okay. So we just finished saying that your body is your responsibility. And now, these verses tell us that our bodies don't even belong to us?

Well, both are true.

Think about something special that you bought (or that your parents bought for you).

WHAT WAS BOUGHT?

WHY DID YOU WANT IT?

HOW MUCH DID IT COST?

Did you know that your body was paid for?

God loves you so much that He wants you to be in His family forever. Because sin separates us from God, someone had to *pay a big price* for us to be close to Him.

In other words . . .

WHAT WAS BOUGHT?

YOUR BODY, YOUR LIFE.

WHY DID GOD WANT IT?

BECAUSE HE WANTED US TO BE IN HIS FAMILY FOREVER.

HOW MUCH DID IT COST?

JESUS' LIFE.

When Jesus died on the cross for our sins, He paid the biggest price anyone can pay for something. His death paid for us to be in God's family forever. And because of that, everything about us, even *our bodies*, is worth something. We're worth a lot, actually. We're worth Jesus' life.

On the next page, write God a thank you note or draw Him a picture that shows how thankful you are that He gave so much so that we could be in His family forever. Let your creativity shine!

- me

Day 3

Going back to the beginning of the week, read our verse for this week out loud.

Now, decorate this part of our verse:

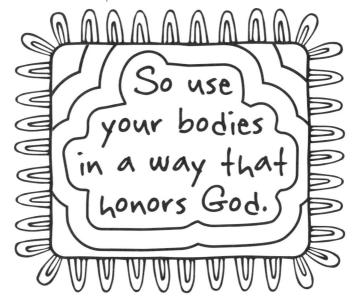

So use your bodies in a way that honors God.

Now, circle the word **HONORS**.

What do you think it means to **HONOR** someone?

Think about your most prized possession. Maybe it's your tablet. Your piano. Your stuffed animal that used to be a bunny but is so old that now it looks like a grumpy old man. Draw a quick sketch of it below:

If you were to let someone borrow or use your most prized possession, you would care about how it was treated. You wouldn't want it to be . . .

- FORGOTTEN
- TREATED BADLY
- DIRTY
- SMELLY
- STICKY

In the same way that we want our prized possessions to be honored, God wants us to honor His prized possessions—our bodies.

THAT INCLUDES . . .

- SHOWERING OR BATHING REGULARLY
- WEARING DEODORANT
- EATING HEALTHY FOODS
- GETTING ENOUGH SLEEP
- SAYING KIND THINGS ABOUT YOURSELF
- SAYING "NO" WHEN SOMEONE MAKES YOU FEEL UNCOMFORTABLE

Looking at the list above, what is one way you can honor God by taking care of your body this week?

_____

"Don't you know that your bodies are temples of the Holy Spirit? The Spirit is in you, and you have received the Spirit from God. You do not belong to yourselves. Christ has paid the price for you. So use your bodies in a way that honors God."

1 Corinthians 6:19-20 NIrV

Day 4

Take some time to think about our verse as you color it in.

Now, take a look at this part:
Don't you know that your bodies are temples of the Holy Spirit?

WHAT DOES THAT MEAN?

So, not only did God send Jesus to pay the greatest price possible for you to be in His family, but He also sent His Spirit to live inside of you—

* ★ **TO COMFORT YOU**
* ★ **TO LOVE YOU**
* ★ **TO GUIDE YOU**

It's pretty cool to think about the Creator of the entire universe living inside of you. Because of that, we should want to take care of our bodies and show our bodies honor and respect.

On the next page is a body. And it's not just any body—it's your body! (Okay, you may need to pretend a little bit, here.) First, grab some colored pencils or markers and deck out your body in a way that best represents you. Give it your hair color, skin tone, and eye color. Then, dress it in your favorite outfit.

Now, let's practice honoring our bodies by complimenting ourselves. In each box, write one thing you like about yourself. *(For example: I love having green eyes because they're the rarest eye color there is.)*

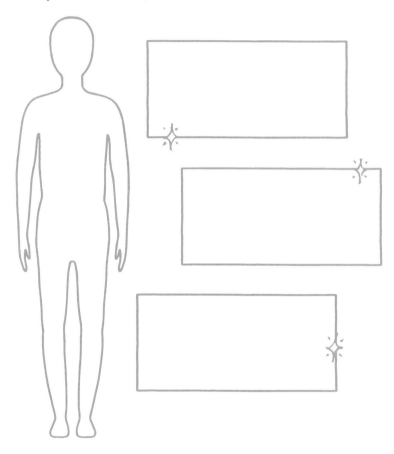

NEVER FORGET: Your body was created by a God who asks you to take care of yourself. To love yourself. To celebrate *you!*

Day 5

Invite your mom for some hang-out time and complete the following activities together.

Activity 1

Discuss together . . .

* ★ IS THERE SOMETHING ABOUT YOUR BODY THAT YOU'VE ALWAYS DISLIKED?
* ★ IS THERE SOMETHING ABOUT YOUR BODY THAT YOU'RE REALLY PROUD OF?
* ★ HAS ANYONE EVER ASKED YOU TO DO SOMETHING WITH YOUR BODY THAT MADE YOU FEEL UNCOMFORTABLE?
* ★ HAS ANYONE EVER ASKED YOU TO EAT, DRINK, OR TAKE ANYTHING THAT YOU WERE UNSURE OF?

Activity 2

Create together . . .

Together, choose one of the following verses and write it down on a sheet of paper or notecard. Make sure you add some color or decorations!

Put the verse somewhere you both can see it. Maybe on the refrigerator door, or on a mirror in a bathroom you both use. Each time you see the verse, say it out loud. Leave it up until you've both memorized it!

"DON'T YOU KNOW THAT YOUR BODIES ARE TEMPLES OF THE HOLY SPIRIT? THE SPIRIT IS IN YOU, AND YOU HAVE RECEIVED THE SPIRIT FROM GOD. YOU DO NOT BELONG TO YOURSELVES. CHRIST HAS PAID THE PRICE FOR YOU. SO USE YOUR BODIES IN A WAY THAT HONORS GOD."

1 CORINTHIANS 6:19-20 NIRV

"HOW YOU MADE ME IS AMAZING AND WONDERFUL. I PRAISE YOU FOR THAT. WHAT YOU HAVE DONE IS WONDERFUL. I KNOW THAT VERY WELL."

PSALM 139:14 NIRV

"'I KNOW THE PLANS I HAVE FOR YOU,' ANNOUNCES THE LORD. 'I WANT YOU TO ENJOY SUCCESS. I DO NOT PLAN TO HARM YOU. I WILL GIVE YOU HOPE FOR THE YEARS TO COME.'"

JEREMIAH 29:11 NIRV

"PEOPLE LOOK AT THE OUTSIDE OF A PERSON. BUT THE LORD LOOKS AT WHAT IS IN THE HEART."

1 SAMUEL 16:7b NIRV

Activity 3

Choose one of the following activities . . .

~ GO ONLINE AND FIND A HEALTHY RECIPE TO COOK TOGETHER.

~ PICK OUT NEW WATER BOTTLES AND DECORATE THEM TOGETHER.

~ PLAN A PHYSICAL ACTIVITY TO DO TOGETHER, LIKE HIKING, SWIMMING, OR ROLLER SKATING.

From One Treasured Girl to Another . . .

Growing up, I had the greatest mom ever! She is so good at taking care of people, especially me! She would make sure that I ate healthy foods, got enough sleep, and washed my face every morning. However, as I got older, those responsibilities started falling on me.

In middle school, I got a cell phone, started sleeping over at friend's houses more, and became more responsible for my own hygiene. I am going to be honest, this new found freedom was not always handled well. I would pretty much eat junk food every time I went over to friend's houses because they had it and I didn't. I would often stay up way too late on my phone, and because of that, I would oversleep and forget to take a shower the next morning.

When my mom noticed these unhealthy habits, she sat me down and explained that I am old enough to start taking care of myself. She showed me Psalm 139:14, which tells us that God made us exactly how he wants us to be. *"I am fearfully and wonderfully made."* She explained that because of that, it is our job to take care of the bodies that He has so graciously given to us.

Understanding that my body is a gift gave me the motivation to take care of it. But it wasn't always easy. I found fun tricks to help me remember to brush my teeth, and I made myself turn my phone off at 8 pm so I would have an easier time going to bed.

Now, I can now see how it is important to take care of myself in order to be the best version of myself. God has called each one of us to do great things, and if I don't take care of myself, I often lack the confidence and energy to fulfill the purposes the Lord has set before me. I am so thankful I practiced good habits when I was in middle school so that now I can be exactly who the Lord made me to be.

God perfectly created and designed our bodies, so it is the least we can do to make sure they are taken care of.

Allie Stanley, Age 20

Notes

_____

_____

_____

_____

_____

_____

_____

_____

_____

_____

_____

_____

_____

_____

_____

_____

_____

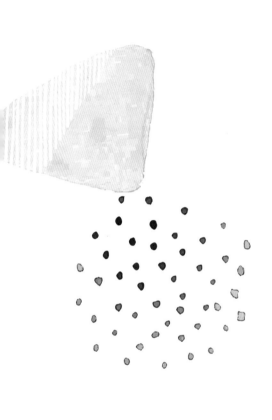

Week 3:

EMOTIONS

BE IN CONTROL OF YOUR ACTIONS, THOUGHTS, AND FEELINGS

Verse:

"Finally, my brothers and sisters, always think about what is true. Think about what is noble, right and pure. Think about what is lovely and worthy of respect. If anything is excellent or worthy of praise, think about those kinds of things."

Philippians 4:8 NIrV

Day 1

Describe a situation where you would use each emoji below in a message to a friend:

_____

_____

_____

_____

_____

_____

_____

_____

_____

_____

_____

_____

_____

_____

The cool thing about emojis is that they help us express emotions. Sometimes, they help us express our emotions better than our words can.

Did you know that some studies say that we have at least twenty-seven different, distinct emotions? That's a lot! And our emotions can change quickly, can't they? We can go from super happy and excited to totally bummed out and annoyed in a matter of minutes.

Having emotions is part of what makes us human. That's how God made us—to be people who have *feelings*.

But there's something interesting about emotions that maybe you've never thought of before. And it's this . . .

OUR EMOTIONS FOLLOW
OUR THOUGHTS.

What we think about affects how we're feeling. When you think about . . .

- ★ the time you didn't get the role you auditioned for in the play.
- ★ when your sister drew on your favorite squishy with a permanent marker.
- ★ all the times we didn't get the grade we wanted.
- ★ that friend who always seems to get her way.
- ★ how your parents keep arguing.

. . . it makes you feel something.

That's why Paul gave us this advice:

"FINALLY, MY BROTHERS AND
SISTERS, ALWAYS THINK ABOUT
WHAT IS TRUE. THINK ABOUT
WHAT IS NOBLE, RIGHT AND
PURE. THINK ABOUT WHAT IS
LOVELY AND WORTHY OF RESPECT.
IF ANYTHING IS EXCELLENT OR
WORTHY OF PRAISE, THINK ABOUT
THOSE KINDS OF THINGS."

PHILIPPIANS 4:8 NIRV

He tells us that we can be in control of our actions, thoughts, and feelings. But, how?

By choosing to think about things that are . . .

* TRUE—WHAT IS FACT OR REALITY
* NOBLE—GOOD, HONORABLE, WORTHY, UPRIGHT
* RIGHT—UNSELFISH, KIND, MORAL
* PURE—CLEAN OR UNPOLLUTED
* RESPECTFUL—FEELING OR SHOWING RESPECT
* EXCELLENT—PERFECT, MATCHLESS, ADMIRABLE
* PRAISEWORTHY—SOMETHING WORTH CELEBRATING

Take a minute and see if you can think of something that IS one of those words.

For example:

TRUE – IT'S TRUE THAT MY FAMILY LOVES ME.

Choose one and write or sketch it in this box.

Spend a few minutes talking to God. Ask Him to help you think about things that are on that list. Write a quick prayer to Him below.

_____

_____

_____

_____

_____

_____

Now, find some time with your mom and ask her to sit down with you for a few minutes and take turns answering the following questions. (Leave your phones/tablets in another room so you can concentrate without distractions!)

- **OUT OF ALL THE EMOTIONS, WHICH IS YOUR FAVORITE TO FEEL?**
- **OUT OF ALL THE EMOTIONS, WHICH IS THE HARDEST TO CONTROL FOR YOU?**
- **WHAT IS SOMETHING WE DO TO HELP EACH OTHER CONTROL OUR EMOTIONS?**

Day 2

We were made to be people who have emotions—lots of emotions. Sometimes, we can feel more than one emotion at a time.

Draw a picture of a face/emoji that would match the mixture of emotions:

HAPPY + SURPRISED = ( )

NERVOUS + EXCITED = ( )

CONFUSED + ANGRY = ( )

Do you ever think of some emotions as good emotions and some as bad ones? Make a list of both below:

GOOD EMOTIONS   **BAD EMOTIONS**

_____   _____

_____   _____

_____   _____

_____   _____

_____   _____

Emotions can feel bad, but did you know there aren't emotions that are actually bad? Sometimes, you can't help what you're feeling. But you can . . .

CHANGE WHAT YOU'RE THINKING ABOUT

and

CONTROL YOUR ACTIONS.

For example, you have homework to do. You know you're supposed to do it before you use technology, but a friend messages you and you want to answer her really quickly. But . . . really quickly turns into 30 minutes and you still haven't started your homework. Your mom finds out and takes away your technology for the rest of the week.

You have a choice to make. You can get upset and . . .

* SIT IN YOUR ROOM, THINKING HOW UNFAIR YOUR MOM IS.
* THROW A FIT AND SLAM A DOOR.
* SKIP THE HOMEWORK TO TEACH YOUR MOM A LESSON.

Being upset is not a bad thing. It's normal, even! God doesn't tell us we shouldn't have certain emotions. He tells us we can choose our thoughts and actions when we're experiencing emotions we don't like. And when we *choose* our thoughts and actions carefully, our emotions become easier to handle.

So, instead of doing one of those three things above, you can choose to do something different. You can choose to . . .

* BE THANKFUL YOU HAVE A PARENT WHO CARES ABOUT YOUR GRADES.
* CLOSE YOUR EYES AND COUNT TO TEN INSTEAD OF BLOWING UP.
* FINISH YOUR HOMEWORK AND ASK YOUR MOM IF YOU CAN HELP WITH THE DINNER DISHES.

Or come up with an idea of your own:

_____

_____

Think through the options. Describe in a few words what the results would be from each situation. Think about your grades, how you would feel, and how your mom would feel.

You can get upset and . . .

SIT IN YOUR ROOM, THINKING HOW UNFAIR YOUR MOM IS.

THE RESULT: _____

THROW A FIT AND SLAM A DOOR.

THE RESULT: _____

SKIP THE HOMEWORK TO TEACH YOUR MOM A LESSON.

THE RESULT: _____

BE THANKFUL YOU HAVE A PARENT WHO CARES ABOUT YOUR GRADES.

THE RESULT: _____

CLOSE YOUR EYES AND COUNT TO TEN INSTEAD OF BLOWING UP.

THE RESULT: _____

FINISH YOUR HOMEWORK AND ASK YOUR MOM IF YOU CAN HELP WITH THE DINNER DISHES.

THE RESULT: _____

Circle the results that would help you. Draw an **X** over the results that would harm you.

Now, decorate the verse. Remember when you're feeling a negative or hard emotion, you have a choice. You can control your thoughts. And you can control your actions.

Color in the words we can focus our thoughts on.

"Finally, my brothers and sisters, always think about what is TRUE. Think about what is NOBLE, RIGHT and PURE. Think about what is LOVELY and WORTHY OF RESPECT. If anything is EXCELLENT or WORTHY OF PRAISE, think about those kinds of things."

Philippians 4:8 NIrV

Day 3

Take a minute to think . . .
When's the last time that you felt:

SAD? _____

SURPRISED? _____

ANGRY? _____

What is your favorite emotion to feel? Draw a picture of
yourself showing that emotion.

Your emotions matter. They are important and they are real.

Have you ever stopped to think about how your emotions affect other people? The people in your class? In your group of friends? In your home?

Check this out. You've seen one of these before, right?

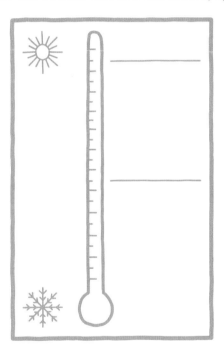

It's a thermometer. We use thermometers to tell us how warm or cool something is.

On the line at the top of the thermometer, write the word **hot**. Now, on the line in the middle of the thermometer, write the words **just right**.

You may not know this, but your emotions are a lot like the temperature. When you're feeling angry, annoyed, and frustrated, the temperature around you gets warmer.

It can feel like turning up the heat in the middle of summer. And just like we have the power to adjust the actual temperature of our house, we have the ability to adjust the temperature of how we feel.

But how do we do that? How do we *not* let our emotions control us? How can we be in charge of how we feel when we often feel out of control?

Look at our verse on page 69. Now, rewrite it below, but use your own words.

_____

_____

_____

_____

_____

_____

When you feel your emotional temperature rising, shift your thinking. Don't react right away. Pause. Take a deep breath. And then focus on things that are good . . .

Think about the following scenarios and give an example of what you can think about instead.

Instead of letting my emotional temperature rise when I bomb a test at school, I can think about good things. I can think about the fact that it's beautiful outside, that I have a family who loves me, and that I got an "A" on my math test last week.

YOUR TURN!

INSTEAD OF LETTING MY EMOTIONAL TEMPERATURE RISE WHEN MY FRIEND AT SCHOOL HURTS MY FEELINGS, I CAN THINK ABOUT:

_____

_____

INSTEAD OF LETTING MY EMOTIONAL TEMPERATURE RISE WHEN MY BROTHER OR SISTER MESSES WITH MY STUFF, I CAN THINK ABOUT:

_____

_____

INSTEAD OF LETTING MY EMOTIONAL TEMPERATURE RISE WHEN MY MOM ASKS ME TO DO SOMETHING I DON'T WANT TO DO, I CAN THINK ABOUT:

_____

_____

Day 4

You can be in charge of your actions, thoughts, and feelings. You can!

Think of the last time you felt your temperature rising. Describe or draw what happened below.

When you sense your emotional temperature rising, there are a few steps you can take to help you take control over what you feel, say, and do.

Replay the situation in your mind that you described above, and let's practice working through it in a healthy way.

1. First, STOP. It's okay to walk away respectfully so that you can think before taking action on what you feel. Walking away helps you be in charge of your emotions. What is something you could you do to remove yourself from this situation? Take a shower? Go for a run? Go to a quiet place?

Draw it here:

2. Now, BREATHE. When you're upset, your body needs more oxygen to help it calm down. Seriously! It's true. The next time you feel upset, pretend you have a mouth full of gum and you want to blow the biggest bubble ever. Take deep breaths in and out. Try it now.
(Take a few deep breaths.)

3. NAME IT. After you breathe, think about some words that describe how that situation made you feel. You can use some of the words in the box or add your own.

_____

_____

_____

_____

_____

FRUSTRATED
OVERWHELMED
SCARED
SAD
CONFUSED
ANGRY
LONELY

Knowing what you are feeling helps you manage your emotions and know what to do next.

4. REFOCUS. Now it's time to try refocusing your thoughts on something good. Something like . . .

* THE LAST MEME THAT MADE YOU SMILE
* YOUR FAVORITE BIBLE VERSE
* A SONG YOU LOVE
* A COMPLIMENT SOMEONE GAVE YOU
* SOMETHING OR SOMEONE YOU'RE THANKFUL FOR

What could you think about?

_____

5. REPAIR. Knowing about and practicing these steps can definitely help us manage our emotions; but as hard as we might try, sometimes we may still blow it and lose control, and say or do something we regret. We're all human.

After calming down, take some time to go back and do any repair work that needs to be done. Is there anyone you might need to talk to or apologize to? What do you think you might say? You can practice here.

_____

_____

_____

_____

_____

_____

_____

_____

_____

_____

_____

Day 5

Invite your mom for some hang-out time and complete the following activities together.

Activity 1

Discuss together . . .

- WHAT MAKES YOU ANGRY? (AND MAYBE EXPLODE?)
- WHAT ARE SOME THINGS THAT MAKE YOU CRY?
- WHO SETS YOU OFF THE QUICKEST AND WHY?
- DO YOU THINK THERE ARE EMOTIONS THAT ARE WRONG OR BAD?

Activity 2

Study together . . .
Take turns looking up the following verses. Talk about which ones might be good to help you keep your emotions under control.

- PHILIPPIANS 4:6-7
- JOSHUA 1:9
- PROVERBS 15:13

Activity 3

Create together . . .
Together, choose one of the verses from Activity 2 and write it below. Decorate it with stickers or markers. When you're at home or in the car, quiz each other to see who can memorize the verse the quickest.

From One Treasured Girl to Another . . .

As a girl growing up in today's world, there is a lot to worry about. For example, do my friends still like me? Do I fit in? Am I good enough? Even down to the smallest little things like, does my hair look good? You might be thinking that you are the only one that worries about all these things, but you are not alone. So many people struggle with it daily. It's one word: anxiety.

But guess what? Jesus has something to say about it all. He says in Matthew 6:34: *"Therefore do not worry about tomorrow for tomorrow will worry about itself. Each day has enough trouble of its own."* (NIV) Jesus is saying that you already have enough to worry about for one day. He wants you to know that He's got tomorrow—you can just focus on today. You only have one today and He wants you to enjoy it. He wants you to stop worrying about what you look like, if your friends like you, or if you are enough to make the team. Jesus wants you to live free because that's why He died. In fact, it says in 1 Peter 5:7: *"Cast all your anxiety on Him because He cares."*

Jesus wants you to give your anxiety to Him because He cares about you, and you are so special to Him.

I have struggled with anxiety since about 3rd grade. I know how hard, frustrating, and overwhelming it can be. Over the past year I have been growing deeper and deeper in my relationship with Jesus, and I have learned a lot. One thing is that sometimes we just need to rest in peace knowing that God is God. After all, He did create the universe. He created you too. When you worry, it's a perfect time to lean in to the truth of who God is and what He did for you. A tip you can use when you get anxious is to write down what's worrying you on a piece of paper. Then, ball it up, rip it, and throw it away. This is a good way to literally give your anxiety to Jesus. By throwing it away, you're giving it to God—and that's exactly what He wants.

So, always remember that Jesus is with you, and He will always be there for you. He can do all the worrying for you, and you can focus on the present day. God's got you, girl, and He loves you beyond what you could imagine. You may want to pray something like this . . .

Dear God,
Thank You for giving me all my emotions even though sometimes they can seem like they are bad. I pray that You would help me to give my anxiety to You because You care about me. I pray that throughout my day, I will not worry about tomorrow but instead focus on today. In Your name I pray.

Anna Christian, Age 12

Notes

_____

_____

_____

_____

_____

_____

_____

_____

_____

_____

_____

_____

_____

_____

_____

_____

Week 4:

FRIENDSHIPS

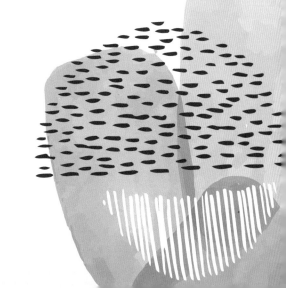

BE THE FRIEND YOU WANT TO FIND

 Verse:

"You are God's chosen people. You are holy and dearly loved. So put on tender mercy and kindness as if they were your clothes. Don't be proud. Be gentle and patient."

Colossians 3:12 NIrV

THE BEST FRIEND I'VE EVER HAD IS

MY FAVORITE THING TO DO WITH MY FRIENDS IS

_____ .

FRIENDS ARE _____

_____ !

Friendships can be the best, right? Everyone wants to have great friends. Friends to talk with, laugh with, and share inside jokes with.

But sometimes, friendships can be *not* so fun. Maybe you haven't experienced this yet. If you haven't, you will. Our friends have the ability to hurt us in ways that other people can't—because when a friend hurts us, it's personal.
But a life without friends would be boring. It would be lonely.

And it would be hard.

So . . .

- ★ **FRIENDS CAN BE FUN.**
- ★ **EVERYONE WANTS FRIENDS.**
- ★ **WE WANT FRIENDS THAT MAKE OUR LIFE BETTER.**

So how do we create and keep good, healthy friendships? Glad you asked!

In the spaces below, write down a few qualities that you look for in a good friend.

_____

_____

_____

_____

_____

_____

_____

Did you know that the Bible talks a lot about friendships? It does! Jesus hung out with a group of people we now call the disciples. They even have their own group name!

Talk about #squadgoals.

Check out our verse for this week. In it, you'll learn the secret to finding a good friend. Read it out loud:

> "YOU ARE GOD'S CHOSEN PEOPLE. YOU ARE HOLY AND DEARLY LOVED. SO PUT ON TENDER MERCY AND KINDNESS AS IF THEY WERE YOUR CLOTHES. DON'T BE PROUD. BE GENTLE AND PATIENT."
>
> COLOSSIANS 3:12 NIRV

Underline the third sentence.

So put on tender mercy and kindness as if they were your clothes.

Now, underline the last two sentences.

Don't be proud. Be gentle and patient.

Those three sentences are the secrets to friendship. And it has nothing to do with *finding* a friend. It has to do with *being* a good friend.

Go back to your list of characteristics of a good friend. Now think—*really* think—about how many of those qualities you show people every day.

Now, no one is saying you have to be perfect. No one is kind 100% of the time. But the Bible makes it clear. If you want to find a good friend, you need to . . .

BE THE FRIEND
YOU WANT TO FIND.

Out of the list you wrote down, which quality comes most easily to you? Describe a situation where you've shown that characteristic to a friend.

_____

_____

_____

Now, find some time with your mom today or tomorrow and ask her to sit down with you for a few minutes and take turns answering the following questions. (Leave your phones/tablets in another room so you can concentrate without distractions!)

* **WHEN'S A TIME THAT A FRIEND HAS HELPED YOU?**

* **WHEN'S A TIME THAT A FRIEND HAS HURT YOU?**

* **WHAT'S THE HARDEST PART ABOUT BEING A GOOD FRIEND?**

* **WHAT'S THE HARDEST PART ABOUT FINDING A GOOD FRIEND?**

Day 2

During our last time together, we learned the secret to friendship. And it's this . . . If you want to find a good friend . . .

BE THE FRIEND YOU WANT TO FIND.

Okay. That sounds great. But, how do you it?!

Remember our verse? Take a minute to read it again. It's on page 89.

If we want to be the friend we want to find, we need to put on "tender mercy and kindness" as if they were our clothes.

HUH?

WHAT?

LIKE A HAT . . . A KIND HAT?

Actually, sort of.

We should treat others so well that it's almost as if we were *wearing* our kindness, patience, and love—like a hat. And that doesn't just mean we're nice to the people we want to be nice to. God wants us to treat everyone this way.

And when we do, our relationships—especially our friendships—are just better.

Think about something you wear every day.

- ⌣ **SOCKS**
- ⌣ **A SHIRT**
- ⌣ **SHOES**
- ⌣ **A HAT**

Choose one of those items to be your **Good Friend Reminder** this week. Each time you put it on, remind yourself that your good-friend qualities should be showing just as much as that piece of clothing you are wearing.

Draw your **Good Friend Reminder** below. (If you're using socks, then draw a pair of socks.) On the inside of that item (or items), write down the names of people you can be a good friend to. On the outside, write down a few ways you can be a good friend.

Color in this week's verse on the next page. Choose a different color for each of the following words:

TENDER MERCY

KINDNESS

DON'T BE PROUD

GENTLE

PATIENT

It's simple, really. God wants us to treat others the way we want to be treated. You've heard that before, right? The Golden Rule.

- **HE WANTS US TO FORGIVE OTHERS (TENDER MERCY).**
- **HE WANTS US TO THINK ABOUT OTHERS' FEELINGS (KINDNESS).**
- **HE WANTS US TO PUT OTHERS BEFORE OURSELVES (NOT PROUD).**
- **HE WANTS US TO KEEP OUR TEMPERS UNDER CONTROL (GENTLENESS).**
- **HE WANTS US TO WAIT WITHOUT COMPLAINING (PATIENCE).**

"You are God's chosen people. You are holy and dearly loved. So put on TENDER MERCY and KINDNESS as if they were your clothes. DON'T BE PROUD. Be GENTLE and PATIENT."

Colossians 3:12 NIrV

Think about how you would show someone each of the qualities of a good friend. Write your thoughts below.

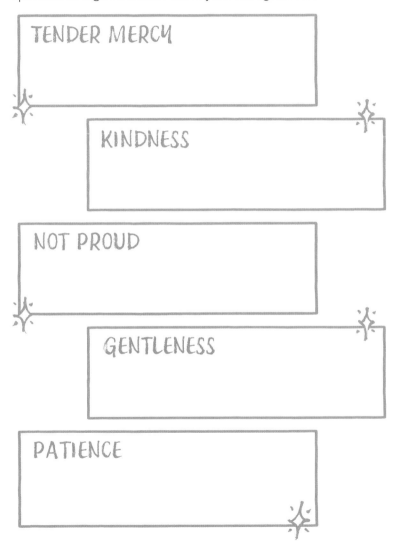

TENDER MERCY

KINDNESS

NOT PROUD

GENTLENESS

PATIENCE

Which qualities of a good friend are the most difficult for you to "put on" as if they were clothes? List two or three:

_____

_____

_____

Choosing one of the words above, use colored pencils, pens, or markers to draw a picture that represents what that word means to you.

Day 4

Fill in the blanks with the names of your friends or family.

MY CLOSEST FRIEND IS _____ .

ONE FRIEND I'D LIKE TO SPEND MORE TIME WITH IS

_____ .

IF I COULD TAKE ANY FRIEND ON VACATION, IT

WOULD BE _____ .

THE FRIEND I ARGUE THE MOST WITH IS

_____ .

I HAVE THE MOST INSIDE JOKES WITH

_____ .

MY FUNNIEST FRIEND IS _____ .

MY FRIEND WHO IS THE MOST LIKE ME IS

_____ .

MY FRIEND WHO IS THE LEAST LIKE ME IS

_____ .

We've learned that the best way to find great friends is to be a great friend. And we do that by putting on good qualities as if they were our clothes. When we do that, our lives *and* our relationships are just better.

But what happens when friendships hurt? Do we still have to keep putting on kindness like a shirt or hat? Do we *have* to be friends with everyone?

Well, the answer is yes. And the answer is also no.

Yes, God still wants us treat others well. But, no, we don't *have* to be friends with everyone.

Has there ever been a time when you felt embarrassed, left out, or hurt by someone? Write about it.

_____

_____

_____

_____

You don't have to spend time with people who make you feel . . .
- **EMBARRASSED**
- **LEFT OUT**
- **LESS THAN**
- **NOT GOOD ENOUGH**

Go back to that last sentence and underline *You don't have to spend time with*.

That's important. You should choose to spend time with people who make you feel . . .

- ﹏ **IMPORTANT**
- ﹏ **FUNNY**
- ﹏ **SMART**
- ﹏ **GOOD ENOUGH**

You should spend time with people you can be yourself around. Because you are amazing and wonderful—every bit of you!

While we don't have to spend time with people who hurt us, God still wants us to be kind to everyone. He wants us to show them kindness, gentleness, and patience.

In the space below, underline all the words that you want to represent your friendships. Then, rewrite them inside the circle.

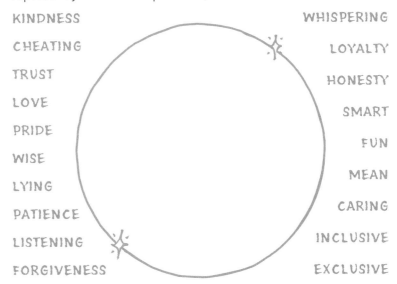

KINDNESS

CHEATING

TRUST

LOVE

PRIDE

WISE

LYING

PATIENCE

LISTENING

FORGIVENESS

WHISPERING

LOYALTY

HONESTY

SMART

FUN

MEAN

CARING

INCLUSIVE

EXCLUSIVE

Day 5

Invite your mom for some hang-out time and complete the following activities together.

Activity 1

Interview each other . . .
What's one of your favorite (moms answer, too!) . . .

* MEMORIES WITH A FRIEND
* WAYS TO SPEND TIME WITH FRIENDS
* THINGS TO WATCH WITH A FRIEND
* STUFF TO TALK ABOUT WITH FRIENDS

Activity 2

Discuss together . . .

* WHAT DOES IT MEAN TO BE THE FRIEND YOU WANT TO FIND?
* WHAT CAN YOU DO THE NEXT TIME YOU'RE IN A SITUATION WHERE A FRIEND HURTS YOU?
* WHO IS A FRIEND THAT YOU HAVE A HARD TIME BEING YOURSELF AROUND?

Activity 3

Create together . . .
Choose one of the following verses about friendship, turn
the page, and create something together using the verse.
Use pencils, paint, markers, stamps, stickers—anything! Talk
together about how this verse can help you be a good friend.

"A FRIEND LOVES AT ALL TIMES. THEY ARE THERE TO
HELP WHEN TROUBLE COMES."

PROVERBS 17:17 NIRV

"LET US CONSIDER HOW WE CAN STIR UP ONE
ANOTHER TO LOVE. LET US HELP ONE ANOTHER
TO DO GOOD WORKS."

HEBREWS 10:24 NIRV

"DON'T DO ANYTHING ONLY TO GET AHEAD. DON'T
DO IT BECAUSE YOU ARE PROUD. INSTEAD, BE
HUMBLE. VALUE OTHERS MORE THAN YOURSELVES."

PHILIPPIANS 2:3 NIRV

Bonus Activity

Create together . . .
Design your **Good Friend Reminder** (from page 92). Choose
a word for the quality of a friend you want to work on. (Moms,
choose one, too!) Design a wearable item, like a bracelet,
T-shirt, or hat. Decorate it with your word, using markers, beads,
paint, stencils, or anything else you find around the house. Wear
your item to remind yourself to be the friend you want to find.

From One Treasured Girl to Another . . .

Have you ever been afraid before, especially when you didn't know how things would turn out? I sure have! When I was ten years old, I moved from Florida to Georgia. I had lived in Florida all my life and all my friends and family lived there too. I had no idea what I was going to do when I moved. I was afraid that I would not make any friends and that I would have a hard time adjusting to a new school. I just wanted to know what was going to happen and how I was going to get through it. I was anxious to see what was going to take place next.

I had to trust God to take care of me because I could not see the future, but I knew God already had plans for me. One verse that really helped me and still does is Jeremiah 29:11: *"For I know the plans I have for you," declares the Lord, "plans to prosper you and not to harm you, plans to give you hope and a future"* (NIV).

I just needed to remember that God would take care of me and would always be there for me. In the next year, I made friends and did great in school. He provided for my family and has given us an amazing home and church to go to. God is strong and He can make miracles happen. He took my nervousness and fears and reminded me that He was in control of everything! I hope that whenever you are afraid, you will remember this, because He is with you no matter what. With Him, you can do it!

Eden Agarwal, Age 11

Notes

_____

_____

_____

_____

_____

_____

_____

_____

_____

_____

_____

_____

_____

_____

_____

_____

Week 5:

TECHNOLOGY

BE WISE WITH TECHNOLOGY

 *Verse*:

"So be careful how you live. Do not live like people who aren't wise. Live like people who are wise."

Ephesians 5:15 NIrV

Day 1

Rank the technology below in order of more awesome to less awesome.

NETFLIX (AND SIMILAR STREAMING SERVICES)

APPS THAT LET YOU ORDER FOOD FOR DELIVERY

VIDEO GAMES WHERE YOU CAN COMMUNICATE WITH OTHER PEOPLE

SIRI AND ALEXA

CARS THAT DRIVE THEMSELVES

SKYPE / FACETIME

SOCIAL MEDIA

GROUP TEXTING

MORE AWESOME

↓

LESS AWESOME

1. _____
2. _____
3. _____
4. _____
5. _____
6. _____
7. _____
8. _____

The thing about technology is that pretty much all of it is awesome, right? I mean, think about this . . .

It wasn't that long ago that people didn't get to choose what they wanted to watch. Then, people had to watch whatever was live on TV. And text messaging didn't even exist. If someone wanted to communicate with their friends, they had to use a phone that was connected to a wall in their house. Plus, they had to share it with everyone in the family. Isn't that crazy?

There are so many cool and amazing things about technology.

What part of technology do you love the most? Texting with friends? Binge-watching your favorite shows? Playing computer games or apps? Write it here.

Even though there's a lot of good that comes with technology, you also know that there are things about technology that aren't so good. In fact, your parents may give you rules about how much you are allowed to use technology. That's because your parents know that even though technology is good, it can also lead to some bad things. Things that could be harmful to you. That's because . . .

TECHNOLOGY IS POWERFUL.

And any time you're dealing with powerful things, you have to be careful.

Even though the Bible was written long ago, we can find some great advice when it comes to dealing with things like technology. Check out this verse and then color or decorate the page.

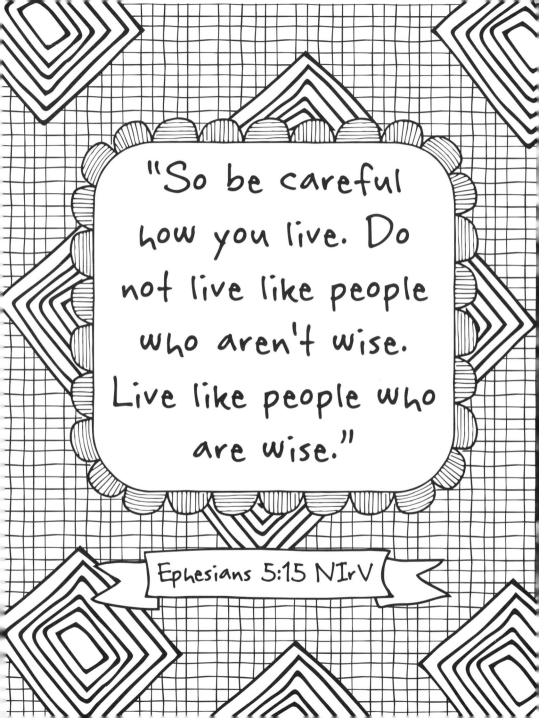

"So be careful how you live. Do not live like people who aren't wise. Live like people who are wise."

Ephesians 5:15 NIrV

The word *wise* isn't one you may use a lot. What do you think when you hear the word *wise*?

_____

_____

_____

When you use wisdom, you use good judgment.

For example, a choice isn't always right or wrong. Sometimes you just have to decide what is wise.

For example,

- ★ SHOULD I STAY UP LATER THAN NORMAL AND WATCH ONE MORE EPISODE OF MY FAVORITE SHOW?
- ★ IS IT OKAY FOR ME TO BE ON THIS GROUP TEXT WHERE OTHER PEOPLE ARE BASHING SOMEONE, EVEN IF I DON'T SAY ANYTHING BAD?
- ★ DOES IT MATTER THAT THE PEOPLE ON THIS VIDEO GAME USE BAD LANGUAGE AS LONG AS I DON'T USE BAD LANGUAGE?

The answer may not always be clear, but it's important to ask:

WHAT IS THE WISE THING TO DO?

Find some time with your mom and ask her to sit down with you for a few minutes and take turns answering the following questions. (Leave your phones/tablets in another room so you can concentrate without distractions!)

DAUGHTER ASK MOM: HOW IS TECHNOLOGY DIFFERENT TODAY THAN IT WAS WHEN YOU WERE MY AGE?

_____

_____

MOM ASK DAUGHTER: WHAT'S ONE PIECE OF TECHNOLOGY YOU CAN'T BELIEVE I GREW UP WITHOUT?

_____

_____

ASK EACH OTHER: WHAT'S YOUR MOST-USED PIECE OF TECHNOLOGY? HAVE YOU EVER BEEN TEMPTED TO USE IT IN A WAY THAT MAY BE HARMFUL TO YOU OR SOMEONE ELSE?

_____

_____

Day 2

If you could design a cell phone exactly the way you wanted it . . .

★ **WHAT COLOR WOULD IT BE?** _____

★ **WHAT APPS WOULD IT HAVE ON IT?** _____

_____

★ **WHAT SONG WOULD BE THE RINGTONE?** _____

_____

★ **WHAT SHAPE WOULD YOUR PHONE BE? (CHOOSE ANY SHAPE YOU WANT!)**

_____

★ **WHAT INVENTIVE UPGRADE WOULD YOU GIVE YOUR PHONE? (FOR EXAMPLE, THE ABILITY TO COOK EGGS OR HAVE A GLITTER DISPENSER.)**

_____

_____

Draw it here:

It's fun to dream about technology because your dreams could one day become a reality. Technology makes it feel like anything is possible.

But too much of anything is too much.

Think about what happens or how you feel when you . . .

- **SKIP HOMEWORK TO WATCH 5 EPISODES OF A SHOW.**
- **SPEND AN ENTIRE NIGHT PLAYING ONLINE GAMES OR APPS.**
- **HURT SOMEONE'S FEELINGS WITH A TEXT OR POST.**
- **SEE ALL YOUR FRIENDS HANGING OUT IN A PHOTO . . . WITHOUT YOU.**
- **COME ACROSS SOMETHING THAT YOU KNOW YOU AREN'T SUPPOSED TO READ OR SEE.**

Technology has the power to shape what we think about others and ourselves. It has the power to affect how we treat others and ourselves, too.

And when it comes to anything powerful like technology, we need wisdom to know how to handle it.

The Bible was written long before Netflix and YouTube, but it can still give us wisdom about how to handle powerful things. Remember our verse you colored in? Look back at page 113 and write it down below:

_____

_____

_____

A long time ago, Paul, the man who wrote our verse, became a follower of Christ a little later in his life—when he was a grown up. Paul went through some pretty crazy stuff. He was blind for a little while, then God healed him and he could see again. Paul was involved in a shipwreck. He was even thrown into jail for telling people about Jesus. Paul had a lot of different life experiences.

It's safe to say that over the years, Paul gained a lot of wisdom. And Paul tells us to be careful. We've heard that before, right? From our parents, grandparents, or teachers.

What are a few situations where you've been told to "be careful?" For example . . .

* **BE CAREFUL USING THOSE SCISSORS.**
* **BE CAREFUL ON THE WATER SLIDE.**
* **BE CAREFUL NOT TO PUT THE ENTIRE BAG OF GUMMY WORMS IN YOUR MOUTH.**

Now add some of your own examples!

BE CAREFUL _____ .

BE CAREFUL _____ .

BE CAREFUL _____ .

Just like you should be careful not to physically harm yourself, you should be careful not to mentally or emotionally harm yourself, too. This is especially true when it comes to technology.

Write down each way you use technology below. (Cell phone, Netflix, Xbox, etc.) Then, write down one way you can be careful when using that technology. Here's an example to get you started.

NETFLIX	NEVER WATCH MORE THAN ONE HOUR IN ONE DAY.
1.	
2.	
3.	
4.	

Day 3

You know what this is, right? It's a stoplight.

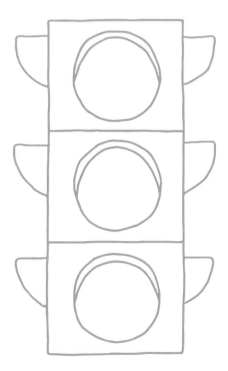

The red light means ————————————————— .

The green light means ————————————————— .

The yellow light means **use caution**.

In other words, the yellow light means . . .

⤳ **PAUSE.**

⤳ **SLOW DOWN.**

⤳ **PAY ATTENTION.**

⤳ **BE CAREFUL.**

⤳ **USE CAUTION.**

If we all used technology wisely, we'd view each time we used it as if there were a yellow light reminding us to . . .

PAUSE.

SLOW DOWN.

PAY ATTENTION.

BE CAREFUL.

USE CAUTION.

Do your parents have any rules when it comes to technology? If so, list those below. If not, what do you think are some good rules when it comes to using technology wisely?

1. _____

2. _____

3. _____

4. _____

5. _____

Grab some markers or colored pencils. Now go back to the stoplight and color in the lights red, green, yellow.

- BESIDE THE RED LIGHT, LIST ONE WAY YOU WILL NEVER USE TECHNOLOGY.

- BESIDE THE GREEN LIGHT, LIST ONE WAY TECHNOLOGY CAN HELP OTHERS.

- BESIDE THE YELLOW LIGHT, LIST ONE WAY YOU CAN BE CAUTIOUS WITH TECHNOLOGY.

Day 4

What's your favorite . . .

SONG? _____

YOUTUBE CHANNEL? _____

TV SHOW? _____

MOVIE? _____

APP? _____

GAME? _____

All of these favorites require technology. Yes, we do need to be careful when using technology. But we can also use technology for good. The key is to be wise with technology.

One way to be wise is to learn all the things God says about using wisdom.

With your mom, look up these verses using your favorite device or on the computer. (Use the search tool and add "NIrV" for the version.) Write down each verse.

PROVERBS 13:20

EPHESIANS 4:29

PSALMS 90:12

From Proverbs 13:20, we learn that if we want to be wise, we need to spend time with people who are wise.

WHO IS A FRIEND WHO MAKES GOOD CHOICES WITH TECHNOLOGY?

_____

Ephesians 4:29 tells us to use our words to say helpful things, to build others up and meet their needs.

WHO IS A PERSON WHO USES THEIR WORDS TO BUILD OTHERS UP?

_____

Psalm 90:12 tells us our lives on Earth don't last forever. Knowing that, we should want to make the most out of the time we have now. That includes not spending all our free time on technology.

WHO IS SOMEONE WHO USES THEIR FREE TIME WELL —SOMEONE WHO IS NOT ALWAYS ON TECHNOLOGY?

_____

Choose one of the people from the list above to reach out to. Ask them to help keep you accountable to being wise with using technology. Ask them if they have any advice to give you on how to use technology with caution.

Day 5

Invite your mom for some hang-out time and complete the following activities together.

Activity 1

Interview your mom and write down her favorite . . .

INVENTION _____

WEBSITE _____

APP _____

SHOW _____

MOVIE _____

SONG _____

WAY TO USE TECHNOLOGY _____

Activity 2

Discuss together . . .

~ WHAT ARE GREAT THINGS ABOUT TECHNOLOGY? AND WHAT ARE THE HARD PARTS?

~ WHY IS IT EVEN IMPORTANT TO THINK ABOUT YOUR REPUTATION OR BEING RESPONSIBLE WITH TECHNOLOGY AT YOUR AGE?

~ WHAT ARE YOU RESPONSIBLE FOR WHEN YOU ARE AWAY FROM YOUR PARENTS? WHAT DECISIONS ARE UP TO YOU WHEN IT COMES TO WHAT YOU SEE, DO, AND HEAR?

~ IS IT HARD TO STAND UP TO YOUR FRIENDS WHEN THEY ARE DOING SOMETHING YOU KNOW IS UNWISE? HOW CAN YOU LEAN ON GOD OR OTHERS TO DO WHAT'S RIGHT IN THOSE MOMENTS?

Activity 3

Create together . . .
Using the next two pages, make a list of goals and boundaries for using technology. There is a page for you and a page for your mom. Though your lists may be a little different, write them both down, and then talk about your lists together. If you see the other person getting off-track, remind them of their list. You could even cut out the page and hang it somewhere in the house where you'll both see it often.

MY TECHNOLOGY GOALS AND BOUNDARIES

MOM'S TECHNOLOGY GOALS AND BOUNDARIES

From One Treasured Girl to Another . . .

Don't you always want to be the one with the coolest and newest technology? I do! I felt like I asked for a phone for forever, but the truth was my parents were trying to protect me and keep me away from things that I don't need to see yet. No matter when you get a phone, it's important to remember that phones (really all technology) can be used for good and bad. And it's all about how we choose to use it.

Did you know that you can use technology for **GOOD**? You can keep in touch with your friends, FaceTime with family, and many other fun things. But there are many ways technology can be used for bad. If you see something that is inappropriate or makes you feel uncomfortable, tell your parents. The best thing to do if you have questions is to go to your parents because they are the safest people to ask! You may think they would get mad at you or take your phone away, but they are here to make sure things are safe and you are out of harm.

Let's say you are at a friend's house and are deciding on a movie to watch, and it is not something you are allowed to watch. Don't play it cool and watch it and then suffer the consequences later. Just go ahead and tell them. You want to feel safe and know you are watching what is allowed by your parents!

Always remember when you are in an unsafe situation, the best thing to do is get out of it and then talk to someone about it. Always remember to be wise with your choices around technology!

"So be careful how you live. Do not live like people who aren't wise. Live like people who are wise" (Ephesians 5:15 NIrV).

Ella DeFeo, Age 12

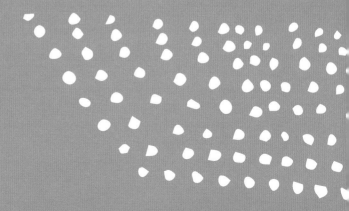

Notes

_____

_____

_____

_____

_____

_____

_____

_____

_____

_____

_____

_____

_____

_____

_____

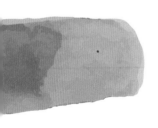

Week 6:

FAITH

BE A FRIEND TO GOD.

ᵔᵔ Verse:

"Come near to God and he will come near to you."

James 4:8a NIrV

Name your top three friends. Below their name, describe how you met them and got to know them.

1. _____

2. _____

3. _____

Maybe you met a friend in 2nd grade. You hung out on the playground, exchanged your moms' phone numbers to schedule play dates, and coordinated outfits. Over time, you found out what they like and don't like, what their favorite food is, and what they enjoyed doing after school.

THE BEST WAY TO GET TO KNOW SOMEONE IS TO SPEND TIME WITH THEM.

Did you know that the same is true with God? Getting to know God is a lot like getting to know a friend. But it doesn't always feel that way, right?

Sometimes getting to know God can feel really hard. Maybe even impossible. It makes sense how to get to know a friend—after all, they can physically sit beside you in class. But getting to know God feels more difficult because you can't see Him or touch Him.

SO, HOW DO YOU DO IT? HOW CAN YOU GET TO KNOW GOD?

Grab your markers or colored pencils and check this out.

James tells us we can get to know God by coming near to Him.

Well that sounds like it should be simple enough, right? But why can it feel so hard? Check the box beside each thought that you've had before:

☐ **GOD FEELS SO BIG AND IMPORTANT. WHY WOULD HE CARE ABOUT ME?**

☐ **HOW CAN I GET TO KNOW SOMEONE I CAN'T SEE?**

☐ **WHEN I PRAY, IT FEELS LIKE NO ONE'S LISTENING.**

☐ **THE BIBLE CAN BE CONFUSING.**

☐ **I'M NOT SURE WHY IT'S IMPORTANT FOR ME TO GET TO KNOW GOD.**

Wanna know a secret? All of these thoughts are totally normal. Most girls your age (and even many adults!) think these exact things.

Getting to know God can feel hard. But like any other relationship, it just takes time. And effort.

We have to do something if we want to grow our own faith.

Now, find some time with your mom and ask her to sit down with you for a few minutes and take turns answering the following questions. (Leave your phones/tablets in another room so you can concentrate without distractions!)

⋆ **WHEN YOU MEET A NEW FRIEND, WHAT'S YOUR FAVORITE WAY TO GET TO KNOW THEM?**

⋆ **WHEN IT COMES TO GETTING TO KNOW GOD, WHAT'S THE HARDEST PART FOR YOU?**

It's okay to have questions. Inside the box, write down all the questions you would ask God if you could.

In your own words, what does it mean to "come near" to someone?

_____

_____

_____

_____

_____

_____

_____

When you come near to someone, you approach them. You move toward them. You take a step their direction.

We are going to talk about four ways you can draw near to God: Hear, Pray, Talk, Live. Let's start with the first one:

HEAR

You hear God's words by reading your Bible.

Circle all the words you would use to describe the Bible.
(Be honest! No one is going to check your answers.)

CONFUSING   ENCOURAGING
COMPLICATED   WEIRD
EXCITING   LONG
HELPFUL   IMPORTANT
BORING   GOD'S WORDS TO US

It's okay to think the Bible is confusing or complicated, but it's also helpful and encouraging. The Bible is one of the best places to look when you want to get to know God.

The Bible has stories about love, adventure, secret spies, and heroes. It also has stories that tell us about God—about who He is and what He's like.

If you don't already read the Bible regularly, it's one of the best things you can do to grow your faith. Here are a few things to keep in mind:

* YOU DON'T HAVE TO START AT THE BEGINNING. THE NEW TESTAMENT (THE SECOND HALF OF THE BIBLE) IS A GREAT PLACE TO START.

* YOU DON'T HAVE TO UNDERSTAND EVERYTHING YOU READ, BUT KEEP READING UNTIL YOU UNDERSTAND SOMETHING.

* AFTER READING THE BIBLE, IT HELPS TO WRITE DOWN ONE THING YOU'VE LEARNED, FOUND INTERESTING, OR HAVE QUESTIONS ABOUT.

Below is a calendar.

- ⌁ FILL IN THE DATES FOR THE NEXT 30 DAYS.
- ⌁ MAKE A GOAL FOR HOW MANY DAYS A WEEK YOU WANT TO READ THE BIBLE. (IT'S OKAY TO START WITH JUST ONE DAY A WEEK!)
- ⌁ MARK THOSE DAYS ON THE CALENDAR.
- ⌁ FOR EACH WEEK THAT YOU MEET YOUR GOAL, COLOR THE WEEK GREEN.
- ⌁ TRACK YOUR PROGRESS OVER TIME.

Month _____ Year _____

Sun	Mon	Tues	Wed	Thurs	Fri	Sat

Day 3

Who is your favorite friend to talk to about . . .

SERIOUS STUFF? _____

SCHOOL STUFF? _____

FAMILY STUFF? _____

GOD STUFF? _____

SILLY STUFF? _____

Talking with our friends is one of the best ways we get to know them better.

Last time we said the first way to get to know God as a friend is to hear about Him. Here's another way:

PRAY

You can talk to God by praying.

Think about your favorite friend. I bet one of the reasons you are close is because you talk to her. You tell her stories. You talk about your life. That's the way you can think about praying. Praying is simply talking to God like you would talk to friend.

You can tell God about . . .

* **YOUR DAY—WHAT WENT WELL OR WHAT DIDN'T.**
* **WHAT BRINGS YOU JOY.**
* **WHAT YOU'RE GRATEFUL FOR.**
* **WHAT WORRIES YOU.**

Remember those questions you wrote down that you would ask God if you could? Well, you can! And whether you believe it or not, God hears you. And more than that, God cares. He cares about the big things and the small things. And when you tell Him about those things, you draw near to Him.

Spend a few minutes talking to God. Tell Him what's going on in your life right now. Tell Him what's going well and what's not going well. Tell Him how you're feeling and what worries or concerns you have.

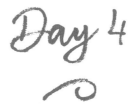

Day 4

Here's another way you can get to know God as a friend. Talk *about* God.

TALK

You can be around others who encourage you to love God. Maybe that's by going to church or being in a small group. Maybe it's spending time with certain friends. When you talk to others about God, you find yourself knowing Him more. You'll find yourself feeling closer to Him.

One person whom you should always be talking about God to is your mom. Maybe you love talking to your mom. Maybe it's hard for you to talk to your mom. But God gave us parents to help us, to guide us, and to encourage us.

Invite your mom for some hang-out time and complete the activities on the next page together.

Activity 1

Interview each other . . .
What's your favorite:

* ★ TIME OR PLACE TO PRAY
* ★ WAY TO PRAY (OUT LOUD, WRITING, DRAWING, ETC.)
* ★ BOOK OF THE BIBLE
* ★ WAY TO FEEL CLOSE TO GOD

Activity 2

Discuss together . . .

* ★ WHAT CAN I DO WHEN I FEEL LIKE GOD IS REALLY FAR AWAY?
* ★ WHAT SHOULD I DO WHEN MY PRAYERS AREN'T ANSWERED?
* ★ WHAT SHOULD I DO WHEN I DON'T UNDERSTAND THE BIBLE OR GOD?

Activity 3

Create together . . .
Write a list of words that describe who God is and put it on the fridge. Share the words with the rest of your family.

Day 5

You come close to God when you live out what you believe to be true about God.

LIVE

How? By not just hearing about God, or talking about God, or praying to God, but by living your life for God—making Him more important than anything else.

Remember when we talked about the qualities of a good friend? That's the friend God is to us. He's the perfect friend. He is generous when we don't deserve it, kind—even when we forget about Him, and forgiving when we mess things up . . .

When we realize and accept the amazing things He has done for us, we will want to be a good friend to Him, and live in a way that shows it.

WRITE SOME THINGS ABOUT WHO GOD IS
THAT YOU ARE THANKFUL FOR.

WRITE SOME THINGS GOD HAS DONE
THAT YOU ARE THANKFUL FOR.

Remember, you are TREASURED and valued as God's creation because of the One who created you. A masterpiece painting is valuable because of the artist who painted it. When you see God as valuable, you want to live life, treat others, and treat yourself in a way that honors God. And when you try to treat others in a way that honors God, you'll find yourself closer to Him.

INSIDE THE CIRCLE, WRITE SOME WAYS THAT YOU CAN LOVE AND SERVE OTHER PEOPLE.

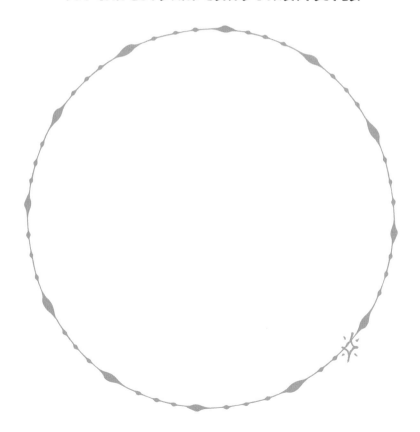

We've talked about 4 ways to get closer to God. By hearing His words, praying to Him, talking about Him, and living it out.

THINK ABOUT THE WORDS HEAR, PRAY, TALK, LIVE, AND WRITE SOME IDEAS ON HOW YOU CAN GROW IN YOUR FRIENDSHIP WITH GOD.

From One Treasured Girl to Another . . .

I want to share one of the coolest things I learned as a little girl about friendship—all thanks to my mom. I had always had really good friends growing up, until I moved to California in 4th grade. It was the first time I ever experienced being lonely, and first time anyone had been unkind to me at school. I didn't know what to do because I had never experienced not having good friends before. I remember coming home from school one day and crying to my mom. She comforted me, and then she taught me the coolest lesson ever: Jesus is the best friend I will ever have.

Sounds kind of funny, huh? Friendship with someone you can't see, sit on the swings with, or eat lunch with.

But here's what I learned: Jesus is truly the best friend I could ever have, and He actually is a friend who sticks closer than a brother or a sister. I learned that through Jesus's sacrifice on the cross, Jesus actually made a way to come to live inside of **ME**—so I actually can talk to Him any time.

I started praying to Him in class, or in my room at night when I was feeling lonely. I found a secret place to run to, whenever I was lonely, hurt, or just in need of friendship.

I started to find friendship with a God who is always there, always present, and always wanting to show me how much He loves me.

I am so thankful that Jesus is a great friend, and place to run to to find the greatest friendship in the whole world!

Caroline Levinson, Age 22

Notes

_____

_____

_____

_____

_____

_____

_____

_____

_____

_____

_____

_____

_____

_____

Congratulations!

Learning to finish what you start is another part of growing up—and you did it! You completed the *Treasured Journal*. Go ahead and give yourself a high-five, fist-bump, or a pat on the back.

FLIP BACK THROUGH YOUR JOURNAL. WHAT'S ONE THING YOU WANT TO REMEMBER FROM EACH TOPIC?

Week 1: IDENTITY

_____

_____

_____

Week 2: YOUR BODY

_____

_____

_____

Week 3: EMOTIONS

_____

_____

_____

Week 4: FRIENDSHIPS

_____

_____

_____

Week 5: TECHNOLOGY

_____

_____

_____

Week 6: FAITH

_____

_____

_____

Completing this journal is a big deal. But putting it into practice is an even bigger deal. If you're ever feeling overwhelmed, lonely, or lost, take out your journal to refresh your mind and heart with God's truth about you:

You are Treasured!

About
the Creators

COURTNEY DEFEO is the founder of Treasured and the mom of two girls. Out of a passion for helping strengthen the relationship between moms and daughters, Courtney began Treasured, an organization designed to help moms and daughters celebrate this special relationship that binds them together. As Courtney says, "Raising daughters can be overwhelming, but it's mostly amazing. You are not alone. All of us are struggling with what to say and do with friendships, technology, body talks, emotions, their identity and much more." It's Courtney's heart that Treasured begins an amazing journey of fun and meaningful conversation for moms and daughters everywhere. For more on Treasured, visit **TreasuredGirlz.com**.

PARENT CUE equips parents to engage with their families and have conversations about things that matter. Parent Cue is a part of The reThink Group, which helps churches partner with families to impact the next generation. For inspiration and resources, visit **theParentCue.org**.

Want more?

Gather a group of your friends and their moms, and have fun talking more about these topics together.

Loaded with even more engaging content and activities, the **Treasured Study** is a 6-session experience connecting moms and daughters about things that really matter.

Get videos, discussion questions, connection ideas and much more at **TreasuredStudy.com**

Dear Mom,

Dear Daughter,

Dear Mom,